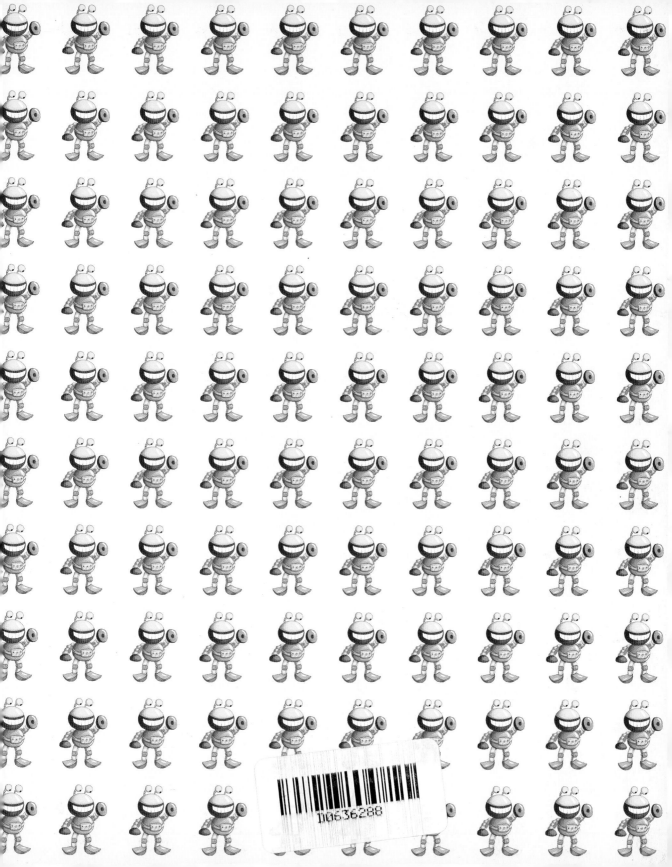

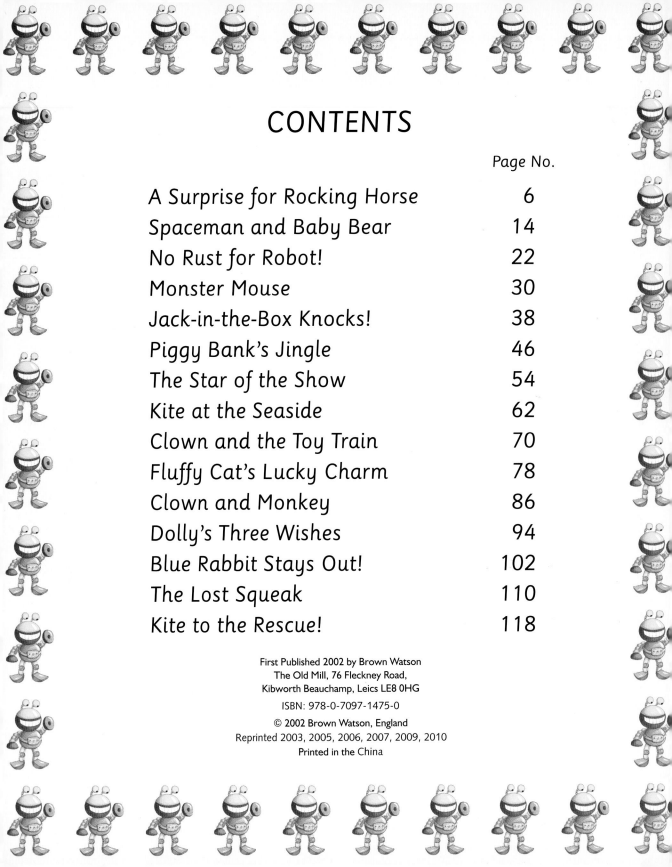

# CONTENTS

First Published 2002 by Brown Watson
The Old Mill, 76 Fleckney Road,
Kibworth Beauchamp, Leics LE8 0HG

ISBN: 978-0-7097-1475-0

© 2002 Brown Watson, England
Reprinted 2003, 2005, 2006, 2007, 2009, 2010
Printed in the China

# NOW I CAN READ

## 15
### Toy Box Tales

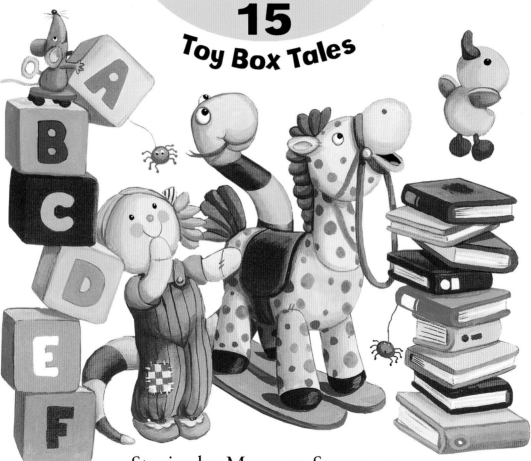

Stories by Maureen Spurgeon
Illustrations by Gill Guile

**Brown Watson**
ENGLAND

# A SURPRISE FOR ROCKING HORSE

Rocking Horse had lived in the playroom for a long time. He liked giving rides, telling stories and just being with his friends.

One day, Dolly came hurrying past.

'Why all the hurry?' he called. 'What is the matter?'

'I cannot stop!' she said. And she went into the Wendy House.

Rocking Horse was puzzled.

'What is going on?' he asked Fairy. 'Dolly always likes a chat!'

'I cannot stop!' said Fairy.

She flew into the Wendy House!

'What IS going on?' said Rocking Horse again. 'Puppets, come and tell me!'

'We cannot stop!' said the puppets. And they went into the Wendy House, too!

One by one, all the toys hurried past. Rocking Horse was very upset. Why had he been left on his own? What was going on?

Still feeling sad and alone, he fell asleep. In his dreams, he felt a blanket being put on his back.

Then, he heard the voices of friends.

'Wake up, Rocking Horse!'

So Rocking Horse woke up. And there he was, with all his friends, a new blanket on his back, and a puppet show about to begin!

'Surprise, surprise!' said the toys.

'You are so nice to us, Rocking Horse!' said Cat. 'We wanted to do something nice for you!'

'Something nice?' said Rocking Horse. 'This is more than something nice! It – it is the most WONDERFUL surprise!'

# READ THESE WORDS AGAIN!

| | |
|---|---|
| lived | hurrying |
| past | matter |
| puzzled | chat |
| cannot | stop |
| alone | dreams |
| around | voices |
| something | surprise |

# WHAT CAN YOU SEE HERE?

wendy house

puppets

rocking horse

friends

blanket

13

# SPACEMAN AND BABY BEAR

Spaceman was at the window, looking out at the night sky.

'I do not like night-time!' said Baby Bear. 'I hate the dark.'

'The night is not ALL dark!' said Spaceman. 'Come and see how brightly the moon shines!'

So Baby Bear went to the window. 'Those stars are so bright!' he said. 'Is that what you look at every night, Spaceman?'

'Yes,' said Spaceman. 'I hope I might see a spaceship, too!'

'What is a spaceship like?' said Baby Bear. 'Is it like a bright, shiny bubble with bright lights?'

'That is right!' said Spaceman. 'How did you know?'

'There is one right there!' cried Baby Bear, pointing. He was right!

The spaceship came closer, its lights flashing. A bright beam of light closed in around Spaceman and Baby Bear. Then, they were in the spaceship!  The light from the moon and the stars made the sky as bright as day. What a fantastic sight!

'I have dreamt of this every night!' Spaceman kept saying. 'Now, it is beginning to get light. Night is coming to an end.'

As he spoke a beam of light inside the spaceship became so bright that he and Baby Bear had to close their eyes tight. When they opened them again, they were back in the house, looking out of the window!

'What a flight!' said Spaceman. 'Are you all right, Baby Bear?'

But Baby Bear was already fast asleep, dreaming of spaceships!

READ THESE WORDS AGAIN!

| | |
|---|---|
| window | dark |
| brightly | shines |
| stars | every |
| might | too |
| shiny | lights |
| right | flashing |
| close | beginning |

# WHAT CAN YOU SEE HERE?

Spaceman

night sky

spaceship

Baby Bear

beam of light

# NO RUST FOR ROBOT!

The bath-toys were in the sink having lots of fun! 'Quack!' went Duck, splashing water.

'Whirr!' went the boat, chasing bubbles.

'Whee!' went Whale, flapping his flippers. 'MUST you be so noisy?' said Rag Doll. 'Robot is not well!'

'It is a touch of rust,' said Robot. 'Rust makes me stiff and clanky.'

'Have a rest in the wendy house,' said Fairy. 'And DO be quiet, bath-toys! Just for a little while!'

'Wheee!' went Whale. 'I shall make some soapy bubbles!' But, as he reached for the soap, it shot out of his flippers and on to the floor!

BUMP! Down went Robot, slipping and sliding on the soap!

'Poor Robot!' said Fairy. 'Can you move? Can you get up?'

'I do not think so,' said Robot.

'Be careful,' said Rag Doll. 'You are lying on the soap!'

The toys tried moving Robot, first one way and then the other. But he was too heavy.

Next, they tried lifting Robot, first one way and then the other.

'Do try to move, Robot!' said Blue Rabbit. 'Just a little bit!'

'I am so stiff,' Robot began. Then he stopped. 'My rusty arm!' he cried. 'I can move it! It is not sore!'

'That arm is COVERED in dirty soap!' said Fairy. 'What a mess!'

'Wheee!' cried Whale. 'The soap got rid of the rust! Robot will not feel stiff and clanky now!'

'No!' cried Robot. 'I feel like a new robot!'

READ THESE WORDS AGAIN!

quack splashing
water flippers
noisy stiff
clanky quiet
little while
sliding careful
heavy first

# WHAT CAN YOU SEE HERE?

soapy
bubbles

Robot

whale

rusty arm

sink

# MONSTER MOUSE

Clockwork Mouse hated not being seen by the other toys!

'Nearly trod on your tail!' said Robot. 'I did not see you!'

'Sorry I bumped into you!' said Spinning Top. 'I did not see you!'

'Sorry I did not say hello!' said Blue Rabbit. 'I did not see you!'

One day, Clockwork Mouse found a mask. He put his wheels inside and it flipped up in front of him. What an ugly monster face!

'Help!' cried Dolly. 'A monster!'

Clockwork Mouse gave a little squeak. The toys were sure to see him now! He tried a monster voice.

'Whooo! I am a monster!'

'Help!' wailed Blue Rabbit. 'There is a monster in here!'

'Whooo!' went Clockwork Mouse again. 'I am a monster!'

'Help!' screamed Baby Bear. 'There is a monster in here!'

He sounded so frightened that Clockwork Mouse felt mean.

'Wait!' he cried. He tried to get out of the mask, but he couldn't.

He was wedged tightly inside.

'A monster!' cried Fairy. 'Help!'

Clockwork Mouse wriggled. He jiggled. Then he pulled. Off came the mask. Robot spoke first.

'Some monster! Clockwork Mouse and a monster mask!'

'Sorry if I frightened you,' said Clockwork Mouse. 'But I wanted to be seen!' He looked so sorry for himself that the toys smiled.

'Well,' said Clown, 'it is nice to know that there is not a REAL monster in here, after all!'

## READ THESE WORDS AGAIN!

hated          sorry
bumped         hello
wheels         flipped
front          ugly
help           squeak
frightened     mean
himself        real

# WHAT CAN YOU SEE HERE?

tail

monster mask

Clockwork
Mouse

face

Blue Rabbit

# JACK-IN-THE-BOX KNOCKS!

Jack-in-the-Box was inside his box!
'Let me out!' he shouted.

Clown undid the catch. Then –
boing! Up jumped Jack!

'Waah!' cried Baby Bear. 'He makes
me jump!'

'Whee!' squeaked Clockwork Mouse.
'He makes me squeal!'

'Whooo!' went Spinning Top. 'He
makes me hum!'

'Back inside the box, Jack!' said
Clown. 'You frighten the toys!'

Poor Jack! Clown did feel sad.

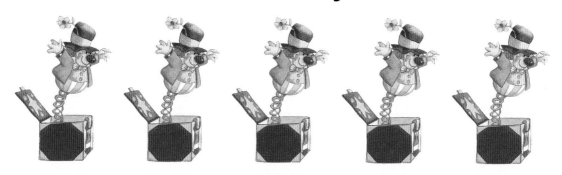

He tapped on the box. 'Jack!' he called. 'Are you all right?'

'Yes!' shouted Jack-in-the-Box.

Clown did not hear him. 'Jack!' he shouted again. 'Are you all right?'

'Yes!' shouted Jack again.

Still Clown did not hear. 'Jack!' he shouted. 'Are you all right?'

'Is Clown talking to himself?' asked Spaceman. 'We must find out!' So the toys went closer.

'Jack!' Clown shouted again. He knocked on the box. Jack knocked back. Knock! Knock!

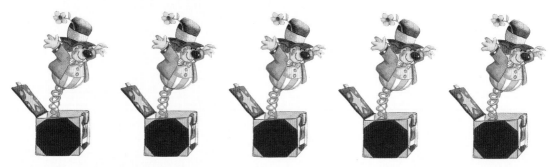

'Jack knocks!' said Clown. 'Out of the box!' He undid the catch and out jumped Jack-in-the-Box!

All the toys cheered!

'Again!' cried Baby Bear. 'Do it again!' So back went Jack into the box. Then – Knock! Knock!

'Jack knocks!' cried Clown. 'Out of the box!' And up jumped Jack.

Now, all the toys like hearing Jack knock. 'Jack knocks! Out of the box!' they cry. And up jumps Jack-in-the-Box.

BOING!

## READ THESE WORDS AGAIN!

| | |
|---|---|
| inside | box |
| knocks | undid |
| catch | jumped |
| frighten | right |
| shouted | closer |
| again | cheered |
| hearing | cry |

# WHAT CAN YOU SEE HERE?

Jack-in-the-Box

Baby Bear

Clockwork Mouse

Spinning Top

Clown

# PIGGY BANK'S JINGLE

'Oh, dear!' said Piggy Bank one day. 'I DO miss my jingle!'

'Your jingle?' said Robot. He was tidying the playroom. 'What do you mean, your jingle?'

'People used to put money in my slot!' Piggy Bank explained. 'The coins made a LOVELY jingle!'

'Now,' he added sadly, 'I am empty. So my jingle has gone.'

'What a shame!' said Robot. He went to pick up a counter off the floor and a dial fell off his control panel!

'What a shame!' said Robot. 'Where can I put this?'

He saw the slot in Piggy Bank's back. 'That is an idea!' he said. And he put the dial in the slot. It made Piggy Bank jingle! Then Robot put in the counter. Piggy Bank jingled again, even louder. Fairy heard him.

'That is an idea!' cried Fairy. 'I shall put this bead from my crown in Piggy Bank's slot!'

'And this safety pin!' said Rag Doll. 'And this hairgrip!' She put them in Piggy Bank's slot.

Piggy Bank jingled again!

'This brass stud has come off my harness!' said Rocking-Horse. 'Put it in Piggy Bank's slot, please!'

'And my spare key!' said Clockwork Mouse.

'And this button!' said Dolly.

A badge, a tag, a ring, a nail – so many things went into Piggy Bank's slot! How glad he was to get his jingle back! And how glad the toys were for Piggy Bank to keep all the things safely until they needed them.

Jingle! Jingle!

READ THESE WORDS AGAIN!

jingle people
money coins
explained empty
shame counter
floor slot
idea louder
harness key
things needed

# WHAT CAN YOU SEE HERE?

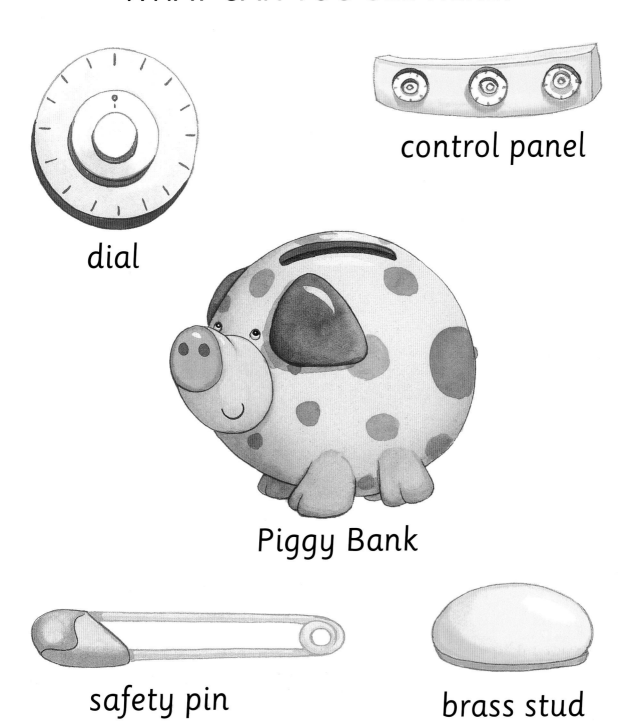

dial

control panel

Piggy Bank

safety pin

brass stud

# THE STAR OF THE SHOW

'We are putting on a special show!' said Pinky Pig. 'And we are going to have a special star! Will you help us, Rag Doll?'

'Ooh, yes!' said Rag Doll.

Rag Doll draped the puppet theatre with green paper. She threaded green creepers on string. She put lots of sand on the stage. She was looking forward to the special show. She might even meet the star!

She looked around at the theatre.

It seemed to shimmer, like waves in an underwater cave.

'Oh...' said Rag Doll in wonder. She touched a coloured fish. Its tail waved, making the green creepers ripple. 'It is like magic!'

Something was shining in the sand.

'A treasure chest!' breathed Rag Doll. She lifted the lid. 'Beads! A bracelet to go on my wrist! And a crown for my head!'

Rag Doll gazed all around. 'What a lovely place,' she said.

The green creepers rippled again.

'It is like a dream...'

There was another sound. It was the sound of clapping!

'What a lovely show!' said Fairy. 'All about a princess finding her crown among the treasure!'

'Princess?' gasped Rag Doll. 'Crown? Treasure?' She turned this way and that, looking around for Pinky Pig. 'But, Pinky, what about the special show?'

'It WAS a special show!' said Pinky. 'Because YOU were the star of the show, Rag Doll!'

## READ THESE WORDS AGAIN!

putting     special

show     draped

paper     string

stage     even

shimmer     touched

ripple     shining

bracelet     wrist

clapping     because

# WHAT CAN YOU SEE HERE?

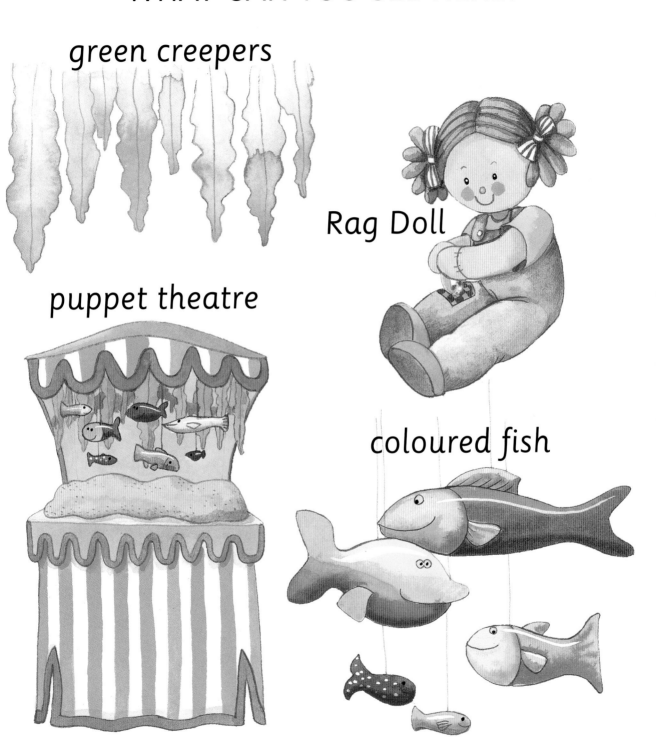

green creepers

Rag Doll

puppet theatre

coloured fish

# KITE AT THE SEASIDE

Kite had been to so many places! High up in the sky on his long string, he had seen green fields and wide rivers and busy roads. Best of all, Kite liked the seaside!

'I just cannot describe it!' he told the toys. 'There is so much to see at the seaside!'

'Maybe,' said Fluffy Cat. 'But none of us will ever see it!'

'What is the seaside like?' asked Clown. 'Can you tell us, Kite?'

Kite looked around.

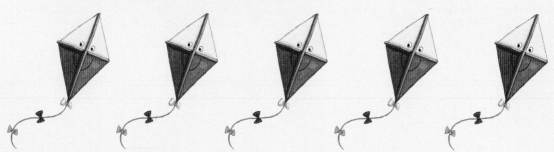

'That tin tray!' he said. 'The sea is like that, smooth and shiny!'

'Put it on the floor!' said Clown. So that is what the toys did.

'Put some bricks on top!' said Kite. 'They can be toy boats!' So that is what the toys did.

'We need a sandy beach!' Kite went on. 'That bit of brown paper at the bottom of the cupboard! Put it on the floor!' So that is what the toys did.

Then Dolly opened her pink umbrella and put it on the beach.

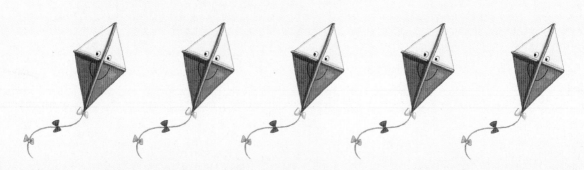

'Now we need pebbles to play with!' said Kite. He looked around again. 'Those bits of jigsaw puzzle can be pebbles! Put them in a heap on the beach! Now we are all at our very own seaside!'

And so they were. Dolly and Fairy sat under the beach umbrella. Blue Rabbit and Clown sailed boats on the sea. Fluffy Cat and Rag Doll played with the pebbles. And, Kite? High up on his long string, he just liked being at the seaside!

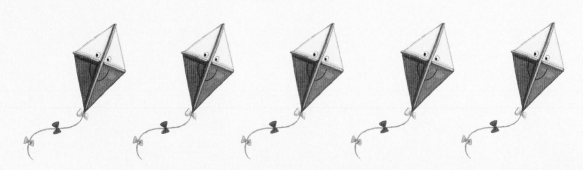

# READ THESE WORDS AGAIN!

| | |
|---|---|
| high | sky |
| string | describe |
| none | smooth |
| shiny | bricks |
| boats | sandy |
| cupboard | floor |
| beach | umbrella |

# WHAT CAN YOU SEE HERE?

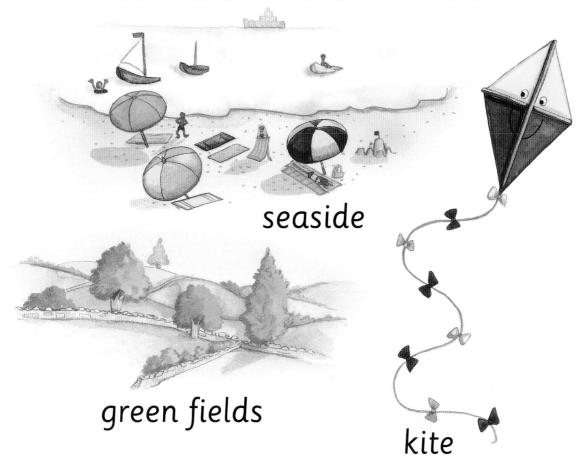

seaside

green fields

kite

pebbles

bits of jigsaw puzzle

# CLOWN AND THE TOY TRAIN

Clown said his hat was magic!

'I take this ball!' he said. 'And I say – Under my hat! Er, Er…' Clown was never sure what to say! 'Er.. I do it like that!' He lifted the hat. But the ball was still there!

'Put your hat on!' said Robot. 'It is your turn to work the toy train! Push the joystick to make it go forward. Pull to make it stop!'

'Pull to go forward,' said Clown. 'Or is it, push?' He pushed so hard that his hat fell off!

It fell over the joystick! 'Under the hat!' he cried. 'Just like that!'

'Aaaagh!' Clown heard yells.

He lifted up his hat – but the joystick had gone! So had the train!

'Aaaagh!' screamed the toys. 'Where are we going?' On and on went the train, shaking and rattling, with cobwebs swaying in the darkness, ugly faces grinning and long fingers clawing at them.

'Aaaagh!' The yells came again.

'Please magic hat!' cried Clown. 'Make the toy train come back!'

It did not sound like magic. But it worked! When Clown looked, the joystick was back under the hat!

He pulled hard. There was a cloud of dust and a screech of wheels, and the train skidded to a stop on the floor! The toys got off, trembling.

'Well,' said Spaceman. 'What a BRILLIANT train ride!'

'It was!' cried the toys. 'Can we have another ride, Clown?'

But Clown had gone to have a rest. The magic train ride had been just a bit too scary for him!

READ THESE WORDS AGAIN!

magic　　　under
never　　　sure
lifted　　　forward
pushed　　　sound
screech　　　wheels
cloud　　　trembling
brilliant　　　scary

# WHAT CAN YOU SEE HERE?

hat

Clown

joystick

 cobwebs

 toy train

# FLUFFY CAT'S LUCKY CHARM

One day, Fluffy Cat found something on the floor. It was round and red, with a hole in the middle. 'What a pretty bead!' she said. 'It can be my lucky charm!'

Fluffy Cat went to pick the bead up, but it rolled into a mouse hole. She reached inside, and – ouch! – she scraped her paw! It did hurt!

'Never mind!' she said. 'I still have my lucky charm!'

But even as Fluffy Cat spoke, the bead slipped from her paw.

'Never mind!' said Fluffy Cat. 'I can soon pick it up!'

She bent down, and – BUMP! – she bumped her head on the windowsill! It did hurt!

'Never mind,' she said. 'I still have my lucky charm!'

She held the bead tightly. But it still slipped from her paw and rolled under a pile of puzzles!

'Never mind,' said Fluffy Cat. 'I can soon pick it up!'

She bent down, and – CRASH! – down fell the puzzles!

'Fluffy Cat!' cried Dolly. 'What ARE you doing?'

'Picking up my lucky charm!' said Fluffy Cat. 'But this red bead has not been very lucky so far! Ooh, my poor head! My sore paw!'

'Red bead?' said Dolly. 'It is the wheel that the wooden horse lost! We have all been looking for it!'

'Never mind, Fluffy Cat!' smiled Robot. 'The little wheel may not have been lucky for you, but it was lucky for the wooden horse that you found it!'

## READ THESE WORDS AGAIN!

round     hole

middle     pretty

rolled     scraped

never     mind

tightly     pile

little     lost

looking     found

# WHAT CAN YOU SEE HERE?

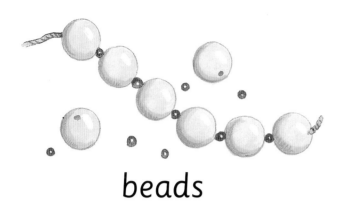

beads

lucky charms

mouse hole

paw

puzzles

# CLOWN AND MONKEY

Clown did like making the toys laugh. He could pull funny faces. He could do funny tricks. And now he was trying to juggle!

'Struggling to do juggling!' he said, as a ball hit him on his nose. BUMP! How the toys laughed!

'I can juggle!' said Monkey. 'And I can throw the balls much higher than you, Clown!'

'Show us, then!' cried Robot.

So Monkey went and stood beside Clown.

'Catch!' said Clown. He threw some balls to Monkey. One, two, three!

'See?' said Monkey. 'I can keep all the balls in the air, without dropping any! One, two, three!'

The toys clapped and cheered.

'Throw me another ball!' cried Monkey. 'And another!'

'One!' He threw a ball up high.

'Two!' He threw another. 'Three! Four! And another! And another! I am juggling with five balls!'

'Monkey,' began Clown, 'wait…'

But Monkey was too pleased with himself to wait for anything!

'Now for the finish!' he cried. 'I catch one ball! Two! Three! Four... and six! Do you think I am the greatest juggler, ever?'

'No!' cried the toys, as the SIXTH ball crashed down on Monkey's head. 'You cannot count, Monkey!'

'But you are still a fine juggler,' said Clown with a smile. 'And you made the toys laugh even louder than I did!'

# READ THESE WORDS AGAIN!

| | |
|---|---|
| laugh | funny |
| could | juggle |
| struggling | higher |
| stood | beside |
| catch | without |
| threw | air |
| cheered | count |

# WHAT CAN YOU SEE HERE?

funny faces

one ball

juggler

six balls

monkey

# DOLLY'S THREE WISHES

Fairy liked being with all the toys.
'I did not like being with the Christmas decorations!' she told Dolly. 'I like being here!'

'Good!' said Dolly. 'Is that really a magic wand in your hand?'

'Yes!' smiled Fairy. 'I can grant three wishes, just by waving it! Make a wish, Dolly!'

'Ooh!' said Dolly. 'I wish I had wings like yours, Fairy!' So Fairy waved her wand – and there was Dolly with silver wings!

'Ooh!' she cried. 'Thank you very much, Fairy!'

'Look at me!' cried Dolly, as she flapped her wings and flew and fluttered around. 'Look at my wings!'

The toys smiled. Dolly did look very funny!

'You will need to rest soon,' said Blue Rabbit. 'You look tired!'

Dolly WAS tired. But when she sat in a chair, her wings dug into her back. She tried to lie down. But her wings got in the way.

Then she tried to rest on a stool.

But she kept falling off! Dolly was in tears.

'Oh, dear!' said Fairy. 'Poor Dolly! You do not like your wings, do you?'

'No,' sobbed Dolly. 'Fairy, can I wish to be just the way I was?'

So Fairy waved her magic wand – and the wings had gone.

'Thank you, Fairy!' said Dolly. 'I am myself again!'

'One more wish, Dolly!' said Fairy. 'What is it to be?'

'I wish for us all to be happy,' said Dolly. 'Just as we are!'

READ THESE WORDS AGAIN!

wish
like
grant
flapped
fluttered
stool
myself

decorations
three
smiled
flew
chair
falling
happy

# WHAT CAN YOU SEE HERE?

fairy

wings

magic wand

dolly

toys

# BLUE RABBIT STAYS OUT!

It had been a long, hot day. The toys had been out in the garden.

'Time to go indoors!' said Dolly.

'It is too hot to go indoors,' said Blue Rabbit. 'I shall stay here!' And he hid behind the rose bush!

'Where is Blue Rabbit?' someone was saying.

'In the toy box, I expect,' said another voice. 'Let us go indoors!'

The door closed. After that, it grew dark very quickly. The moon cast strange shadows.

Soon, the wind began to blow. Blue Rabbit wished he felt braver!

He trod on something slimy! Ugh! It was a worm, slithering down into a hole in the ground!

'Silly me!' said Blue Rabbit. 'I... I... what was that?' He had heard the patter of paws. Two pointed ears and a pointed nose appeared.

'A fox!' cried Blue Rabbit. 'Oh, p-p-please do not eat me!' But Fox did not want to eat a toy rabbit!

'Miaow!' went the cat. She picked Blue Rabbit up carefully in her mouth!

She carried him to the cat-flap!

'I am not one of your kittens!' he cried. 'Put me down!'

By the time they got inside the cat-flap, Blue Rabbit was so tired. He closed his eyes...

'Another fine day!' said a voice. 'And, here is Blue Rabbit, all ready to go into the garden!'

Blue Rabbit blinked. Had he really been carried by a cat, scared by a worm and chased by a fox?

'No...' he told himself. 'I must have sat in the sun for too long!'

# READ THESE WORDS AGAIN!

garden      indoors
someone     saying
closed      quickly
strange     wished
braver      slithering
pointed     appeared
carried     tired
blinked     chased

# WHAT CAN YOU SEE HERE?

fox

Blue Rabbit

rose bush

cat-flap

shadows

# THE LOST SQUEAK!

Squeaky Snake had lost his squeak!

Robot banged him on the back. Fairy squeezed him tight. But his squeak had not come back.

Sadly, Squeaky wandered about. Suddenly he heard the thump of big feet. He looked up to see two tusks and a long, grey trunk among the thick, green plants.

'Am I in the jungle?' gasped Squeaky.

'A balcony is as good as a jungle for an elephant without a trumpet noise,' came a voice.

'A trumpet noise?' said Squeaky. 'Was it like this?' He blew on a whistle. A tinny sound came out.

'No,' smiled Elephant. 'That is not like my trumpet noise.'

'Was it like this?' said Squeaky. He blew on a bubble pipe. A bubbly sound came out.

'No,' Elephant smiled again. 'That is not like my trumpet noise!'

'Was it like this?' said Squeaky. He took a balloon and blew and blew until – BANG! The balloon burst! And Squeaky gave a squeak!

'SQUEAK! My squeak is back!' he cried. 'Squeak! SQUEAK!'

But, Elephant was laughing too much to listen! 'Ha-ha! HA-HA!' Then, 'Tara-Tara! TARA-TARA!'

'SQUEAK!' went Squeaky. 'You have got your trumpet noise back!'

'TARA-TARA!' went Elephant.

'You have got your squeak back!'

Now, just to make sure that Squeaky can squeak and Elephant can make a trumpet noise, they make each other laugh! SQUEAK-SQUEAK! TARA-TARA!

READ THESE WORDS AGAIN!

| | |
|---|---|
| squeak | banged |
| squeezed | tight |
| wandered | thump |
| tusks | trunk |
| noise | voice |
| sound | bubbly |
| blew | burst |
| laughing | listen |

# WHAT CAN YOU SEE HERE?

Elephant

balcony

Squeaky Snake

whistle

bubble-pipe

# KITE TO THE RESCUE!

The toys called him Windmill Man. He was fixed to the garden fence, winding a wheel. The more the wind blew, the faster Windmill Man wound his wheel.

One day, a strong wind began to blow. Indoors, it rattled the doors and shook the windows. Outside, it howled across the garden.

There was a loud CRACK and Windmill Man broke away from the fence! Up into the air he went, his wheel banging on the window.

'What was that?' said Dolly.

'It is Windmill Man!' said Baby Bear. 'Look! The wind is blowing him higher and higher!'

'What can we do?' cried Fairy.

'Unwind my string!' said Kite. 'Slide me through the window!'

So the toys unwound the string and slid Kite through the window. As they let out his string, he flew higher and higher.

'Windmill Man!' Kite shouted. 'I will fly as near to you as I can! You must get hold of my string!'

Windmill Man reached out bravely. How he grabbed Kite's string he never knew. But he did.

'Clever Kite has done it!' shouted Spaceman. 'Pull in the string, Robot!'

The more they pulled the string, the closer Kite and Windmill Man came. At last, they squeezed in through the window together.

'What a rescue!' said Windmill Man. 'Thank you, Kite!'

'Thank YOU, Windmill Man!' said Kite. 'I have always wanted to fly in a really strong wind!'

## READ THESE WORDS AGAIN!

fixed        winding

wheel       wind

wound     strong

howled    broke

unwind    slide

closer      through

rescue     really

# WHAT CAN YOU SEE HERE?

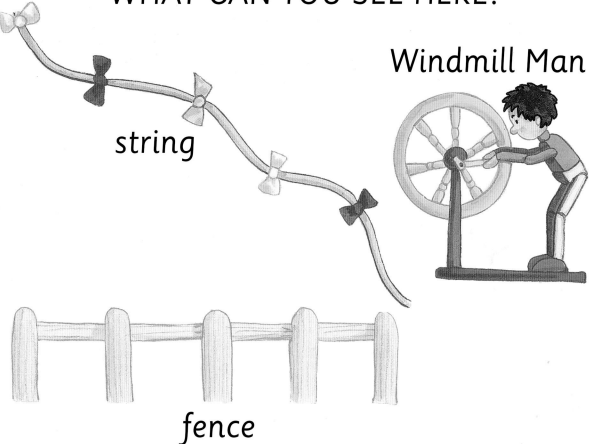

string

Windmill Man

fence

door

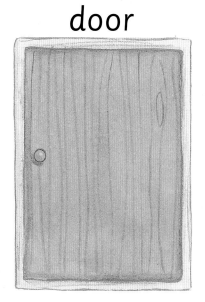

window

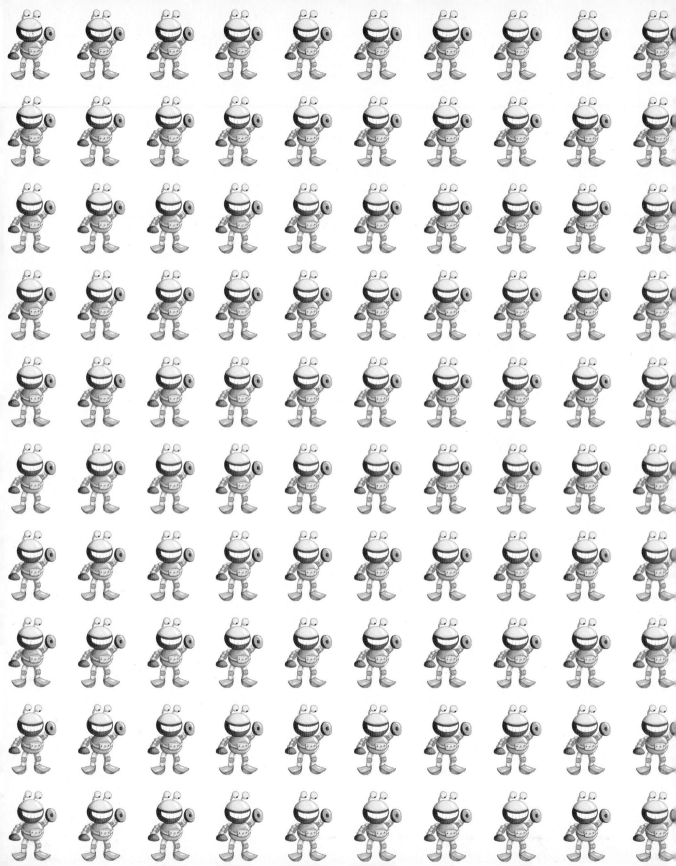